THE
CITY &
SOUTH LONDON
RAILWAY

by
T.S. Lascelles

THE OAKWOOD PRESS

© The Oakwood Press 1987

ISBN 0 85361 360 5

Printed by S & S Press, Abingdon, Oxford.

First Published December 1955
Second Printing 1987

Published by
The OAKWOOD PRESS
P.O.Box 122, Headington, Oxford.

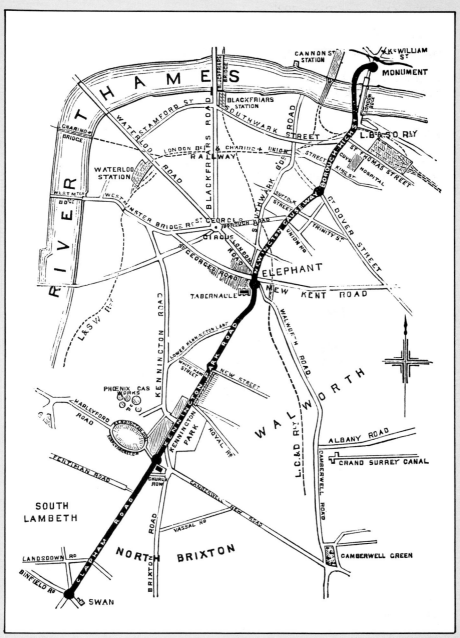

The original route map of the City and South London Railway.

Courtesy "The Engineer"

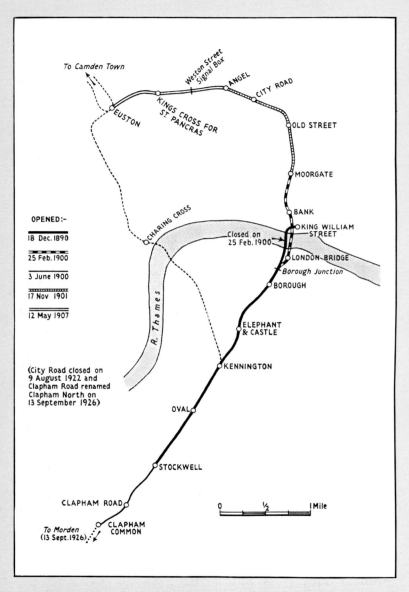

The City & South London Railway: showing also extensions made after incorporation into the Underground group.

THE CITY & SOUTH LONDON RAILWAY

THE City & South London Railway, the earliest of London's " tube " railway lines, came into being to meet the demand for quicker and more convenient travel than the steam-worked underground and suburban railways and the horse-drawn omnibuses and tramcars of the 1870s and 1880s could provide. In 1864 the Metropolitan Railway, which had been opened in the previous year, carried 11,720,000 passengers and the London General Omnibus Company, established in 1856, 42,650,000. Ten years later, in 1874, the respective figures were 44,120,000 and 48,340,000, with 20,770,000 on the Metropolitan District Railway and 41,930,000 on the trams. In 1884 the omnibuses (including those of the new London Road Car Company) conveyed 78,170,000, the trams 119,260,000, the Metropolitan and the District together 114,450,000: a total of 311,880,000 journeys by these means of local public transport, or 78 journeys a year per head of the population, in comparison with 18 journeys per head in 1864.

The first attempt in London to escape from steam as motive power for underground railway transport came in the early 1860s, when a company was promoted to build a pneumatic railway, working on the principle of the so-called pneumatic despatch tube which is still in fairly general use, to run from Scotland Yard, Whitehall, to Waterloo station. Some £60,000 was expended on the project, but the London & South Western Railway failed to get powers to subscribe to the undertaking, and during the financial crisis of 1866 it was abandoned.

Another early proposal for providing a comprehensive system of communication below the level of the streets, without having to follow the awkward cut-and-cover method of construction adopted for the Metropolitan Railway, was put forward by an eminent civil engineer of the day, Peter William Barlow, resident engineer for the construction of the South Eastern Railway. While sinking the cylinders for the Lambeth Bridge he conceived the idea of propelling similar devices horizontally for the purpose of tunnelling. This was a development of the original shield idea advanced by the elder Brunel at the time of the Thames Tunnel works. Barlow's tunnels were to be lined with iron and to have liquid cement injected to fill the space, kept as small as possible to avoid subsidence, left around the tunnel lining as the cylinder was propelled forward, stage by stage, by means of screw jacks. Barlow patented his shield in 1864, and in 1867 he published a pamphlet advocating a system of " omnibus subways ", formed of 8-ft.-diameter iron tunnels, in which were to travel steel " omnibuses "—tramcars they would be considered now—holding 12 passengers each, propelled by manpower aided by gravity. Fares were to be collected in the cars. The stopping-places were to be all at one level on any one route, and to provide for the differences of surface level in the various districts it was proposed to have three series of subways at different levels, the cars and passengers being transferred up and down by lifts.

Barlow and Greathead

The only immediate outcome of these proposals was the formation in 1868 of a company to build a tube tunnel under the Thames just west of the Tower of London. In this work Barlow was greatly aided by one who had been his pupil, the South African, James Henry Greathead, who assumed the responsibility of carrying out the work as contractor. The subway was opened in 1870. Costing about £10,000, it was 6 ft. 7 in. in clear internal diameter and 1,350 ft. long, with 10-ft. circular shafts at each end, some 50 to 60 ft. deep. The minimum depth of the tube below the river bed was 22 ft. Steam-driven lifts were placed in each shaft, and a small tramcar on a track of 2 ft. 6 in. gauge holding 12 persons, was worked to and fro by a cable and two 4-h.p. steam hauling engines. The number of passengers these facilities could convey was not sufficient to cover the charges, and the subway was soon converted into a footway, with spiral staircases in the shafts. It continued to serve in this capacity until the opening of the Tower Bridge in 1894, since when it has been used as a runway for hydraulic pipes.

In 1870 Barlow obtained an act authorising the construction of another such subway between the City and Southwark, a little west of London Bridge. This was to be 8 ft. in diameter and 1,200 yd. long. It was to be worked on the same methods as those adopted in the Tower Subway, but their failure there made it impossible to raise the required capital, and the project was abandoned in 1873. Work on another subway was begun in 1876 between North and South Woolwich but not completed.

In 1882 the Charing Cross & Waterloo Electric Railway Company was authorised. The proposal was to build a line from Trafalgar Square to Waterloo station, with double-line tunnels each end and iron tubes under the Thames. The civil engineers were Henry Law (who had been appointed by the Court of Inquiry to inspect and report on the fallen Tay Bridge early in 1880) and George Chatterton, with Dr. C. W. Siemens, of Siemens Brothers and Co., as electrical engineer. A prospectus was issued in 1883, showing a share capital of £100,000 and borrowing powers up to £33,000. A tender had been received from Kellett and Bentley for completing the civil engineering in 18 months for £80,000; a contract was to be made with the Siemens firm for the rolling stock and electrical equipment and for working the line. Some 60 ft. of tunnel under Northumberland Avenue and the Embankment had been built by the time the prospectus was issued.

In 1884 a London Central Railway Company sought powers to make an electric line from the northern end of the Waterloo line via Oxford Street to St. Martins-le-Grand, but the House of Commons Committee declined to accept the preamble of the bill, saying it had supported the earlier railway as an experiment and wished to await proof of its success before agreeing to other similar schemes. In July 1885, however, the Charing Cross & Waterloo Railway was abandoned.

Meanwhile Greathead had become interested in the advance made by cable traction on tramways, which first appeared in London, following the work of Hallidie in San

Francisco and other American cities, on Highgate Hill in 1884. He thought that the endless cable system, which enabled traffic in both directions to be worked on separate tracks and the vehicles to be stopped and started individually at will, was likely to be especially suited to underground lines built on the tube principle, where steam locomotives were, of course, out of the question. He also thought that the cable system would prove much more economical than steam and would enable underground lines to pay a good return. He accordingly joined in obtaining an act in 1884 authorising the construction of a twin-tunnel subway from a point near the north end of London Bridge to the Elephant and Castle. Shortly afterwards a company was formed, under the title of City of London & Southwark Subway Company, with an authorised capital of £300,000, to carry out the work; Greathead was engineer, with Sir Benjamin Baker and Sir John Fowler as consultants. There was great opposition to the bill; it was largely owing to the skill with which Greathead gave his evidence in committee, supported by Sir Benjamin Baker, that it was eventually passed. The promoters of the undertaking invited Charles Grey Mott, who had been associated as a director with the Mersey and Severn tunnels, and a director of the Great Western since 1868, to become chairman of the new company. The first directors were C. S. Grenfell, S. Hanbury, A. Hubbard, and W. Robinson (both Great Western directors), with H. H. M. Smith as Secretary. (Mr. Grenfell remained a director for nearly 40 years, until his death early in 1923.)

Mr. Mott, having visited the Tower Subway, became fully convinced that the work was practicable and interested himself with much energy in getting the construction started. The prospectus said that 12 per cent dividend might be expected. The principal cable traction patents were being exploited in Great Britain by the Cable Tramways Corporation, and the subway company paid a considerable sum for the rights.

Construction of the Line

The site selected for the City terminus was where King William Street crosses Arthur Street (East and West) now named Monument Street; the station building was No. 46 King William Street, close to the Monument. Except where Hibernia Wharf and Chambers were unavoidably passed under, on the south side of the river, the route intentionally followed the public streets throughout, in order to avoid interference with private property. In consequence, the line curved sharply round on leaving the terminus and, running below Arthur Street West, approached the river under Swan Lane, at the end of which Old Swan Pier then stood. This thoroughfare is so narrow that the up line tube had to be placed over the down to keep them within its width. Curving round again to reach the Borough High Street, opposite the end of Denman Street, at the south end of London Bridge, the route continued under Newington Causeway to the proposed Surrey side terminus at the Elephant. There were to be intermediate stations at Denman Street and Great Dover Street, Borough, the total distance being slightly over a mile and a quarter.

In March 1886 plans were far enough advanced for the company to place an order with a Liverpool contractor, Edmund Gabbutt, and work was begun by erecting a temporary staging behind the Old Swan Pier and sinking a shaft, from which a start was made on 28 October 1886 with driving the upper, or up line, tunnel southwards under the river. The down tunnel was begun below the up in March 1887. It was driven to come alongside and west of the up line tunnel south of the river, thus placing the two lines in a right-handed position at that point, which it reached in June. In driving the up line tunnel northwards to the King William Street site the London clay was pierced, and a certain portion had to be constructed under compressed air, until the clay was again met with. In their report dated February 1887 the directors record to their satisfaction that " a new Thames tunnel should have been finished in about 15 weeks from its commencement ". They hoped that the line would be ready to open before the end of the same year. They had come to the conclusion that the route was rather too short to develop the real carrying capacity of the line—and had accordingly deposited a bill for an extension to Stockwell, making it

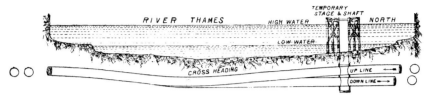

Section of the Thames crossing of the City and South London Railway.

Courtesy "The Engineer"

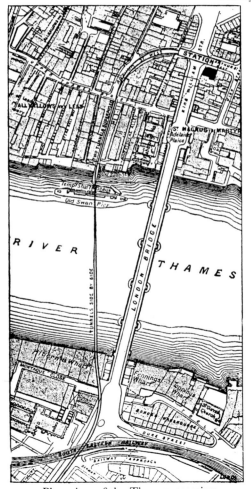

Plan view of the Thames crossing.

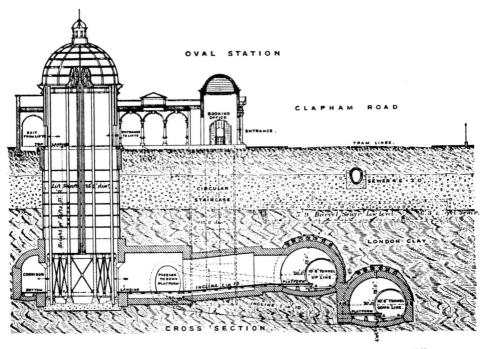

(*Above*) Cross-section of the Oval station, showing the running lines at different levels to minimise walking distances. (At Borough and Kennington the upper line is farther from the lifts.) (*Below*) Section of the tunnel and carriage section.

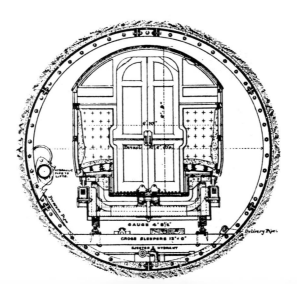

just over three miles long. The proposed station at the south end of London Bridge had been abandoned, for the time being, at least; the Brighton Railway Company declined to come to terms over the covered way connecting their station with the one on the subway. This is hardly surprising, for there would have been little inducement to Brighton line passengers to descend by lift, merely to be taken to the other end of the bridge and ascend again there, on their journey into the City.

Shafts and Tunnels

On completion of the tunnels under the river, land was acquired for the Borough (Great Dover Street) and Elephant stations, and operations were begun by sinking the 25-ft. diameter lift shafts, to be used to begin the tunnelling. The shaft at the City station had to be begun from within a heavy building, whose walls were only just far enough apart to contain it; it was carried down to a depth of 75 ft. through made ground, gravel and clay. The erection of temporary shafts in the streets, although allowed by the act, was hedged round with great restrictions; it was found, however, that there was no need to use the powers, the work being successfully done from the station shafts; in spite of this the alignment of the tunnels was accurately achieved; the opposite borings met with exceedingly small error, which was highly creditable in work of such a pioneer character and on an awkward route. The temporary shaft in the river proved of great service in making the City section of the line and the King William Street station; all excavated materials, iron, bricks, etc., were conveyed through it, not only towards the City but southwards for some distance. It was finally bricked up and made watertight over the up line tunnel, and the staging at the back of the pier was taken away.

In their report of July 1887 the directors announced that the act for the Stockwell extension had been passed and authorised additional capital of £300,000. Great public interest was being taken in the construction of the subway. The plans so far formed for the cable working comprised an engine house at the Elephant, driving one cable at 10 m.p.h. on the City section and another at

12 m.p.h.—the route being much easier—on the Stockwell section. For this reason the tunnels on the latter were to be 10 ft. 6 in. in diameter, instead of 10 ft. 2 in. on the first part of the route. The contract for the extension was given to Walter Scott & Company, who soon began operations at the two intermediate station points, New Street, Kennington, and Oval (Kennington Church), as well as at the Stockwell terminus. Contracts were shortly afterwards placed for the lifts at the stations, with Sir W. G. Armstrong Mitchell (later Armstrong Whitworth) & Company. Edmund Gabbutt, the contractor for the City section, was unable to complete the work there owing to ill health, and the contract was transferred to Walter Scott & Company. The total cost of land, including that at Stockwell, where it was now proposed to place the workshops and propelling machinery, was less than had been estimated.

Contracts had been arranged for the supply of the cable traction equipment, but since the promotion of the undertaking electric traction had made its appearance as a rival to cable working and had been applied on tramways in America and, to a small extent, elsewhere. The Bessbrook & Newry electric railway had been opened in Ireland in 1885; this was a much more ambitious concern than any before attempted, and its working was successful. In consequence Mr. Mott, to whom suggestions had been made in the technical press, began to doubt whether cable haulage would be the best to use in the subway. Maximum speed was limited to about 12 to 14 m.p.h.; beyond that wear and tear on the cable would be prohibitive. Shunting and making up trains was very difficult, and the most complicated apparatus, including auxiliary cables, had been necessary on tramways to get anything like reasonable facilities. Electrical working would be very much more flexible, approximating to ordinary railway conditions, and it offered the possibility of a higher average speed. In the half-yearly report for August 1888, the board told the shareholders that these points had been exercising their attention and said: " After much careful investigation, and after obtaining the best technical and engineering advice, the directors have come to the conclusion that electrical force, conveyed by continuous conductors, offers the best solution of the difficulty. Several eminent firms have made proposals for the working of the line in this way, and negotiations are going on with the view to some practical trial of the system, before a decision is arrived at."

Electric Working

The first proposals received, one of which came from an American firm, were merely general and so divergent in character that it was not easy to compare their merits. Offers were therefore invited on the basis of a specification, covering the running of a three-minute service, and tenders were received from some of the firms concerned, with proposals in some cases for actually working the railway. The half-yearly report for January 1889 stated that " after exhaustive examination " of them, aided by " the valuable assistance of Mr. C. E. Spagnoletti, an experienced electrical engineer ", the board had decided to place a contract with the well-known engineering firm of Mather & Platt, Ltd., then of Salford Iron Works (now Park Works), near Manchester, whose electrical department "is under the immediate direction of Dr. Edward Hopkinson, who has had exceptional experience in electric traction ". The contractors undertook to provide the power necessary to run a three-minute service from each station at a greater average speed than that attained on the Inner Circle of the Metropolitan Railway, and they guaranteed also for a period of two years the cost per train mile at a considerably lower rate than if steam locomotives were used.

In a note to the report Greathead stated that the experimental train, provided for in the contract, was expected to be ready in April 1889. The tunnelling was complete from the City to the Oval station. C. E. Spagnoletti, to whom the report made reference, was the telegraph superintendent of the Great Western Railway; he had been appointed consulting electrician to the subway, probably in the first instance in connection with signalling and lighting, and this selection evoked some mild criticism in the press on the ground that his experience was confined to telegraphy. He would, of course, have been well known to the chairman and two other directors associated with the Great Western, and this no doubt led to the decision to seek and take his advice.

Matters did not progress quite so quickly as had been hoped. Difficulties were encountered near Stockwell with wet gravel, requiring compressed-air working, but in July 1889 the shareholders learnt that a start had been made with the boiler house at the power station and that rails were laid from the City to the Borough, ready for the trial train, and the rest of the track was being pushed on. Early in December 1889 experimental running was begun with a locomotive and two carriages over the completed track, using a small temporary generating set at the Borough station, and one tunnel was through to Stockwell by the beginning of 1890. A second locomotive arrived in February 1890 and on 7 March the Lord Mayor and other distinguished guests travelled from the City to the Elephant, where Greathead explained the leading features of the work. Their return journey was delayed for an hour, as the local water company's turncock had shut off the water to the boiler feeding the generating set in consequence of some defect; this materially deranged the luncheon which had been prepared at the City station for the august visitors. A week later the directors of the Metropolitan Railway were also invited to a private view of the line. The incline tunnel at Stockwell, connecting the station with the depot alongside Spurgeon's Orphanage in the Clapham Road, with a gradient of 1 in $3\frac{1}{2}$, was also ready. Locomotives and trains were hauled up this incline by cable and moved about in the depot by capstans, a practice which continued for some years.

The report of January 1890 said: " As the present authorised lines stop at Stockwell, about a mile short of the great centre of traffic meeting near the ' Plough ' at Clapham, your directors have deemed it advisable to deposit a bill in Parliament asking for powers to extend the line to that point. . . . They propose also to alter the name of the company to that of the City & South London Railway Company, as being more in harmony with the present nature and object of the undertaking." The report also noted the promotion of what later became the Central

London Railway, from a point in Bayswater to a junction with the C. & S.L.R. at Arthur Street West. "As at present proposed, this would not be satisfactory to this company, but it is possible that arrangements may be made to effect a junction between the two lines beneficial to both companies." This first C.L.R. bill was thrown out, and nothing more was heard of a junction with that line. The report also said that it had been thought expedient to apply for powers to acquire land and make the station at London Bridge (Denman Street*), originally intended. Greathead was able to report that " the satisfactory working of the line by electricity has been placed beyond doubt by the important series of experiments carried out by Messrs. Mather & Platt on the City section of the line with one of their locomotives and the Ashbury Company's carriages ". Many shareholders were by now wondering how long it was still to be before their property began earning some return, and the chairman had to express regret about the delays. They were invited to an inspection of the trial train and locomotives about this time.

By July 1890, the date of the first report bearing the new name of the undertaking, almost everything was ready; two of the generating engines and dynamos were installed and one working; the hydraulic engines for providing the lift power were ready; part of the rolling stock had arrived. The tunnels were everywhere complete, and a train had been run the whole length of the line. The Clapham extension bill had received the Royal Assent. It authorised the proposed change of name and a further increase of capital of £200,000. The signalling was said to be almost finished, and the locomotives were arriving regularly.

The Opening Ceremony

A formal opening ceremony was performed by the Prince of Wales, afterwards King Edward VII, accompanied by his eldest son, the Duke of Clarence, on 4 November 1890. He was received at the City terminus by the chairman and directors and, descending in the lift, was handed a handsome gold key bearing the arms of the company on the

* Now London Bridge Street.

The Prince of Wales (later King Edward VII) seen here at the formal opening of
Stockwell station on the 4th November 1890.

Author's Collection

A fine view of locomotive No. 1 and carriages of the original "padded cell" type, at Stockwell depot before the opening of the line.   *London Transport*

A close up of locomotive No. 1 showing the detail of construction well. This locomotive was built by Mather & Platt in 1889.   *London Transport*

A front view of locomotive No. 1.   *London Transport*

Locomotive No. 11 as later fitted with side windows.   *London Transport*

Inside view of locomotive No. 31 (Crompton built) showing the sparse interior.
London Transport

Locomotive No. 36 (Crompton 1900) as refurbished for preservation at Moorgate station. It was damaged by a bomb on 29th December, 1940.   *London Transport*

handle, with which he operated a small switch, giving the signal to turn on the current to the mains. A distinguished party, including the Lord Mayor and Sheriffs, was present and after inspecting the electric locomotive, No. 10, specially painted in cream and French grey and named *Princess of Wales*, and the carriages, the royal guests were conveyed to the Oval station to inspect the equipment there. Proceeding to Stockwell they were entertained to luncheon. The neighbouring streets were gaily decorated, and in the evening the workmen were entertained to supper.

On the same day the company received the authority of the Board of Trade, after an inspection made by Major-General Hutchinson and Major Cardew, as electrical adviser, for conveying the public, but it was decided to have some further weeks' private working. After one or two premature announcements, the public service began on Thursday, 18 December 1890. T. C. Jenkin, formerly audit accountant, London, Tilbury & Southend Railway, had been appointed general manager in May. Mr.— later Sir—Basil Mott was resident engineer, at first for the Stockwell extensions and later for the whole line.

The original arrangements on this first electric tube railway are of considerable interest. The station tunnels on the original City to Stockwell line were excavated and lined with brick to a depth of 3 ft. The two termini had tunnels 26 ft. wide by 20 ft. high; at the intermediate stations each line had its own tunnel, 20 ft. wide by 16 ft. high and about 200 ft. long. At King William Street there was a further length of brick tunnel, somewhat smaller in diameter, before the tubes began in which the up and down lines converged to a single line of rails in the centre of the station, with a platform on each side. This layout formed part of the original cable-working plans, no other terminal arrangement being possible with it without considerable complication. At Stockwell there was an island platform with a line on each side and a scissors crossing between the station and the tubes The incline tunnel from the depot connected with the down line on the City side of the scissors, with a short spur siding accommodating a locomotive. Both termini had hydraulic buffers.

Station Layouts

No two intermediate stations were quite alike. Only at
the Elephant were the up and down lines on the same level;
this enabled a crossover siding, long enough to hold two
trains, to be built connecting the lines north of the station.
At the Borough, Kennington, and the Oval the two lines,
although side by side in plan, were at different levels, the
up line being 9 ft. 6 in. higher than the down. At the
Borough the direction of traffic was right-handed, the down
tube, which left King William Street in the normal left-
handed position, running under the up at Swan Lane and
passing to the right-hand—or " wrong "—side of it after
the river shaft, then recrossing under it between the
Borough and the Elephant. At the Borough the two
station tunnels were level with each other in plan, but at
Kennington and the Oval they were displaced, as much as
half the station length at the latter. Each station had two
hydraulic lifts in one shaft, each holding 50 persons, and
an emergency spiral staircase; the station at King William
Street was under the roadway and was reached by a length
of straight staircase first. The station buildings, designed
by T. Phillips Figgis, were of neat and pleasing form, with
domes over the lift mechanisms; at the City, 46 King William
Street was modified inside to receive the equipment.
Passengers paid their money at turnstiles. Gas lighting was
used at first, as there was insufficient reserve of electric
power.

The permanent way consisted of 60-lb. flat-bottom
rails, spiked to cross sleepers resting directly on the tube
without ballast (which was dispensed with to avoid dust
as much as possible). Although giving rise to some
resonance, this track gave entire satisfaction. The curves
were in places rather severe, but this could not have been
avoided without taking an entirely different route. The
worst curves were met immediately after leaving the City,
on turning into the Borough High Street, and north of the
Elephant station. There were also some very awkward
gradients. The down line fell at 1 in 14 soon after leaving
the City, on a sharp curve, to come below the up, which
approached the terminus at 1 in 40 and 1 in 70. Just

Stockwell station at the opening.

The Island platform at Stockwell station.

Kennington Oval station.

The Elephant and Castle station.

All views courtesy "The Engineer"

north of Swan Lane it had an S-curve and there fell for a
short distance at 1 in 150, presumably to assist trains round.
If cable working had not been originally intended, there is
little doubt that the City station would have been placed
rather deeper, so giving easier gradients. At most but
not all stations there was a short down grade of about 1 in 30
to assist trains in accelerating. The longest piece of level
track on the line, about 600 yards long, was north of the
Elephant, which was the deepest station, though the down
part of the Borough station was practically as deep, and the
line rose on the whole thence to Stockwell, where it was
only 43 ft. below the street to rail level. The lowest point
of all was under the river shaft on the down line.

The power station at Stockwell, lying to the east of the
Clapham Road, was a brick building, 141 ft. by 44 ft.,
with three—soon afterwards four—450 h.p. vertical non-
condensing compound engines by John Fowler & Co., of
Leeds. The cylinders, of 17 in. and 27 in. diameter by
27 in. stroke with 14 ft. diameter 14-ton flywheels, were
fed at 140 lb. pressure from six—later eight—28 ft. by
7 ft. Lancashire boilers and drove, by belt and jockey
pulley, Edison-Hopkinson type compound generators,
capable of delivering 450 amperes at 500 volts when
running at 500 r.p.m. These dynamos weighed 17 tons
and had an electrical efficiency of 96 per cent. The series
coils could be partially or wholly short-circuited by special
switches on the frames. The switchboard was of very
simple construction and arranged for connecting any of the
generators to the four feeders, independently or in parallel.
The feeders had fusible cutouts and quick-acting safety
switches, which threw a resistance into circuit if the current
exceeded a certain value. Two feeders were coupled in
parallel as far as the track at Stockwell station, whence
one continued to the Oval. The two others ran to the
Borough. These cables were supplied by the Fowler-
Waring Co., with 61/14 strands, lead-sheathed, taped and
compounded.

The third rail was divided into sections and connected
through fuse boards in the signal boxes. This rail was of
special high-conductivity steel of channel section, weighing
10 lb. per yd., carried on glass insulators in the four-foot,

not in the centre, owing to the central buffers on the trains coming so low, but about a foot from the right-hand running rail (looking towards the City). It had originally been intended to have an overhead conductor, but space did not permit. The locomotive frames being very near rail level, the conductor rail was deliberately set 1 in. below it, wooden slopes being provided at the points to carry the collector shoes up and across. At the Stockwell scissors crossing, movable interlocked conducting bridges were installed to provide a continuous path for the shoes.

The power station also contained three pumping engines for supplying the hydraulic lift mains, which were carried on brackets inside the tunnels and worked at a pressure of 1,240 lb. per sq. in., and twin air pumps for maintaining a reservoir at Stockwell station charged to 80 lb. pressure, for supplying the trains with air for the Westinghouse brakes.

The power equipment and the circuits were thus of the simplest description. Near the power station was a loco-motive and carriage shed, with lines connecting with the incline tunnel from the various tracks. At one end of the engine house was a locomotive repair bay.

Locomotives

The electric locomotives, of which there were 14 at first, carried a cab with end doors, resembling those used on steam tram engines, on a four-wheeled frame measuring 14 ft. over the centre buffers. They were driven by two series-wound motors with Gramme armatures, each able to develop 50 h.p. at 310 r.p.m., or 25 m.p.h., with 27-in. wheels. These armatures were mounted directly on the axles, an arrangement originally suggested by Sir William Siemens, but not previously used. Both motors were permanently connected in series and controlled by a plain rheostat switch and reversing switch. The starting current was 150 amperes and starting drawbar pull 2,050 lb. The average running current was 50 amperes. A cast-iron flap-type collector shoe was placed at each end of the locomotive. There was no air pump for the brake, but two large reservoirs under the cab sides, sufficient for about 30 stops from full speed, were recharged after a down

A pen and ink sketch of the interior of the locomotive and carriage shed at
Stockwell.   *Courtesy "The Engineer"*

Longitudinal section of the locomotive of the City and South London Railway.
                                                           Courtesy "The Engineer"

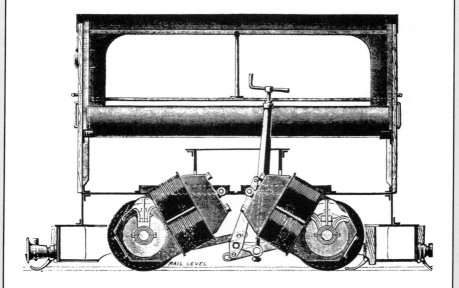

RAIL LEVEL

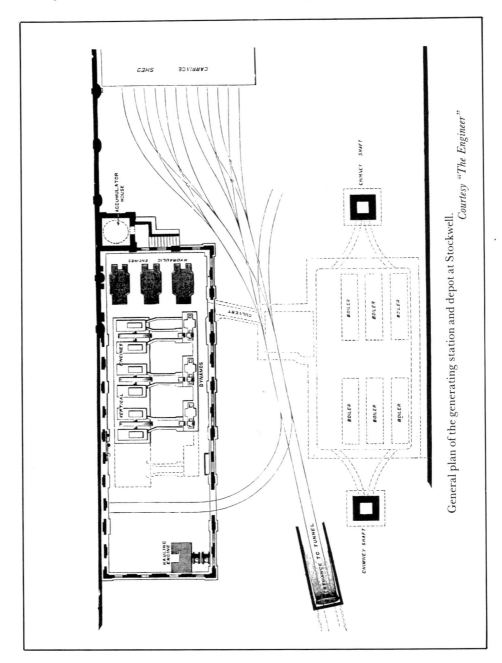

General plan of the generating station and depot at Stockwell.

Courtesy "The Engineer"

Locomotive No. 36 seen here with the renovated original trailer car No. 10.
Author's Collection

The Stockwell depot in September 1922 with locomotive No. 37. *Oakwood Collection*

A side view of trailer car No. 20, built by Thames Ironworks in 1898.

London Transport

The intermediate type of trailer car with the lower and larger windows. Note the bogie and connecting arm.

London Transport

An original Ashbury trailer car as refurbished for preservation. *London Transport*

The sparse and claustrophobic interior of the "padded cell" type trailer car.
London Transport

A close up of an original driving axle, showing armature mounted on the axle.
Author's Collection

Locomotive No. 8 inside the workshops, showing the later type of motor mounting.   *London Transport*

journey from the Stockwell reservoir. There was also a
powerful hand brake. The train pipe was carried along the
tops of the locomotives and carriages. The second of
the two locomotives provided for the first trials on the City
section had geared motors, but it proved extremely noisy
and difficult to haul if out of order and was kept for
emergency work only. The locomotives were originally
painted a red-brown, but very soon a handsome bright
yellow livery, somewhat similar to that used by Stroudley
on the Brighton line, was adopted.*

Thirty bogie carriages of the tramcar type, with longitudinal seats for 32 persons, were provided by the Ashbury
Carriage & Iron Company. They were comfortably
upholstered, high up at the back, and had very narrow
windows indeed; but these were later made larger and the
upholstery reduced. They gained the nickname of
" padded cells " and weighed about 7 tons; the interior
measured 7 ft. from floor to roof. The bogie frames were
prolonged beyond the bodies to support small guard's
platforms provided with collapsible gates. Each carriage
had four electric lamps and two emergency oil lamps. A
train consisted of three carriages, with two guards, who
closed the end doors and attended to the gates. A loaded
train weighed about 40 tons and ran at an average speed,
including stops, of 11½ m.p.h. For a few years the guards
worked enamelled indicator plates, introduced in 1891,
showing the name of the next station, through an oblong
opening in the end door. It was very difficult, with the
small windows, for passengers to tell where they were.
In the course of time more vehicles were obtained from
various builders, but for many years there was no real
change of design, apart from minor constructional details.
The exterior of the vehicles had varnished wood finish
and was not very pleasing; it soon began to look unattractive
and contrasted strangely with the smart look of the engines
after the yellow painting came in.

Signalling

The signalling was entrusted to the then well-known, but
now defunct, firm of Dutton and Co., of Worcester; it was

* For details of locomotives and carriages, see the Appendix.

of the mechanical type then customary. A special design of signal, however, was necessary to meet the restricted space available in the tubes. Clearance was small also at the stations, especially at Stockwell, where starting, engine, and other shunt signals had to be mounted on a gantry outside the signal box in rear of the scissors; very short semaphore arms were used. This box had a 24-lever frame, that at King William Street 9 levers. The only intermediate box controlling both directions of traffic was at the Elephant, where the up siding outlet points were key-locked. The lines being at different levels at the other stations, separate up and down boxes were necessary, so that the Elephant box had four block bells. Each station was protected by a home signal—there were no distants—as an emergency signal, and the block sections extended from starting signal to starting signal, or to the buffers at a terminus. C. E. Spagnoletti provided a special design of his lock-and-block apparatus operated over two line wires, the bell being rung on one polarity and the block release transmitted on the other, in each direction, with his rail deflection treadles at the ends of the sections. The block indications were " Train Arrived " (green screen), and " Train on Line Going ", for section in advance, or " Train on Line Coming ", for section in rear (red screens). The signal and light repeaters were of his usual type. There were two single-needle speaking circuits, with connection to the power station, and telephones from box to box were soon added. Primary batteries provided the power for the signalling, which underwent important modifications, mentioned later, soon after the line was opened.

The new venture in London locomotion was a pronounced success from the first day, 18 December 1890; over 10,000 people had passed the turnstiles at King William Street by 7.0 p.m. Many were, of course, attracted by the novelty of the undertaking, but regular travellers along the route gladly resorted to the much quicker means of getting to work and back. There was a uniform fare of 2d. for any distance, and this was seized on by sections of the press as a violation of the Parliamentary trains requirement; the company was, however, specially exempt from that obligation. A five-minute service was run on weekdays only, but a Sunday service, beginning about midday, was put on from Sunday, 5 April 1891. The equipment functioned on the whole extremely well, and the company's report dated February 1891 said: " There is every reason to be satisfied with the use of electricity as a motive power." An average of 15,000 passengers a day travelled on the line. The fourth engine and generator, which Major Cardew had recommended, were soon obtained. The principal trouble experienced was the burning-out of locomotive armatures, due to some extent to the form of winding used, combined with the overload caused by the carriages weighing rather more than was at first proposed, but improved winding methods overcame this trouble before long. The lighting of the trains was not very satisfactory. Even the electrical press felt constrained to say that this was not up to the mark and complained that the lamps were only " red hot " as the trains ascended the gradient into the City. Improved power supply and voltage regulation remedied this but it was some time before the lighting was really good.

Handling the heavy traffic at King William Street proved a considerable difficulty, and the need for other stations in the City was at once apparent. A bill was therefore deposited for a " branch line " from the City station to the Bank and Moorgate Street and thence to the Angel, Islington; it did not pass, however. The lack of underground siding accommodation at Stockwell was found to be a great handicap. Plans were made to construct some, and quite extensive sidings were provided there. The City terminus was badly located; people coming from most parts of the City had to negotiate a very awkward and crowded street crossing to get to it, but as the station could not deal with the traffic at certain hours this was possibly not a serious matter.

In June 1891 the fares were altered to give a 1d. fare from some stations at certain hours of the day. Season tickets were introduced and the year saw the arrival of two new locomotives from Siemens Bros. & Co., with drum armatures, Nos. 15 and 16. These proved very useful. The difficulties at the terminus still increasing and giving rise to much complaint, both from passengers and share-holders, " owing to its confined dimensions and steep incline leading to it "—the chairman even felt constrained to call it " an engineering blunder "—a bill was deposited in 1891 to provide a London Bridge station, with two new tunnels under the river and easy inclines to a central station at the corner of Lombard Street and thence to the Angel. The original intention seems to have been to make the new station on the existing line and begin the new tubes just north of it, but the bill was held over and did not pass until 1893, when powers were obtained for new tubes leaving the existing ones just north of the Borough station (London Bridge station being on the new route) with an increase of capital of £750,000. Basil Mott became chief engineer in place of Greathead, and two directors, W. Robinson and A. Hubbard, were succeeded by S. Barclay Heward and Edwin Tate. By the beginning of 1893, 11,357,162 passengers had been carried. The company leased the adjacent building in King William Street, in order to add a ladies' waiting, luggage, and parcels rooms to the City station; but they took no steps to use the powers to extend to Clapham, really fearing to encourage more traffic for a time.

Shortening the Sections

The traffic that offered itself, however, had to be carried, and it was soon found that the block sections were too long to enable it to be worked without delays, especially at the City terminus. With only one line, no second train could be brought in while one was there, and this could not leave until the line was clear to the down starting signal at the Borough, some 1,330 yards away. The section between the Oval and Stockwell was also as long.

In February 1892 the Board of Trade sanctioned the introduction of an up outer home signal at the Oval and a down outer home at the Borough, with the additional electric treadles required. As soon as a train had reached the treadle in advance of his outer home a signalman—after putting the signal to danger, of course—could operate his block instrument and release the starting signal in the rear. An additional electric locking instrument controlled the section of line from the outer home to the starting signal. In July 1893 a down outer home was provided at Stockwell, combined with a " last vehicle " treadle. This was in reality an insulated plate on the side of the tunnel, with which a brush on the last bogie of the train made contact, completing the block release circuit through the rails, so giving a positive last vehicle action, the first of this kind to be found on an underground railway. (The first instance of a positive last vehicle action for controlling signals, in this case automatic ones, on a line in the open was apparently seen under the Timmis system at the opening of the Liverpool Overhead Railway on 6 March 1893.) These " treadles " in due course replaced the rail deflection type throughout the line. By February 1894 all stations had been fully provided with outer home signals. That at King William Street, about 600 yards out, could only be worked satisfactorily over the awkward curves by using lengths of gas barrel along the tunnel side to guide the wire.

The oil lighting of the signals in the tunnels was found unsatisfactory; the strong draught produced by the trains often put them out. Gas was tried but proved little better; it was therefore decided to adopt electric lights for all signals. The signals which required repeating were equipped with a circuit designed by Basil Mott and the assistant engineer, P. V. McMahon (who became chief engineer in 1895, when Mott went to the Central London), with which the signal lights could burn only if the position of the signal mechanism agreed with that of the lever in the signal box; a red and green luminous repeater was provided to show what the signal indication was, and this acted as a pilot to prove that all lamps were burning. This arrangement became standard. The signalling so modified was, with small alterations in detail, also used on the extensions of the line, and it remained unaltered until superseded many years later by automatic signalling. The Central London line also was fitted with similar equipment. In later years separate block sections were created between inner home and starting signals at some stations, to facilitate the working of the traffic, as, for example, at the Oval on the up line and the Elephant on the down. In the last days of this signalling, after the 1914 war, as many as 28 trains per hour were being handled by it.

An Experimental Motor-Coach Train

The heavy morning and evening traffic made it advisable to add a fourth coach to the trains, but this was only possible with the King William Street layout if the separate locomotive bringing a train in and the turnover one backing on could be got rid of. It had originally been intended to have motors on the coaches, but the Board of Trade had insisted on separate locomotives when the line was planned. Space restrictions also pointed to that course as being the better. In 1894, however, the directors reported that they had " instructed their engineer to make experiments with a view to substituting motors on the train itself in place of the present locomotive, with the object of adding a fourth coach to each train ". By January 1895 they were able to state that, although some difficulty had been experienced in making the train negotiate the sharp curves into the City terminus, it had been completed and had been approved by the Board of Trade. It was intended to convert all the carriage stock on this plan. The project went no further, however. It was found that time was lost with this train at the King William Street station, as the driver and his assistant had to make their way through the crowded platform and often were not ready to start when the signal was given to do so. No technical information appears to have been published about this interesting motor train experiment.

In addition the traffic difficulties arising from the single platform line there led to a scheme being got out to alter the layout to an island platform and two lines, as at Stockwell terminus, and the work was completed by the end of 1895. The available platform length had to be shortened somewhat to allow room for the scissors crossing, and there was not room for the four-coach motor train. The adoption of motor coach trains would also have made more sidings imperative at Stockwell, since a defective train would have to be shunted complete, whereas a locomotive could be disposed of in a space of about 15 feet, its carriages remaining available. It was also thought that different-powered trains would be wanted directly the proposed extensions were open, and that made it inadvisable to make any change at the moment. The locomotive system therefore remained in use, and indeed did so until the line was entirely rebuilt some 28 years later. After the disastrous fire on the Paris Metropolitan Railway in 1903, in which 84 people perished, the company issued placards pointing out that the electrical equipment on their trains was on a separate locomotive, which could be uncoupled and run clear if required.

The rush-hour traffic continued to grow, so much that the company was compelled to raise the fares between the hours of 8.0 and 10.0 a.m. It became evident that the City terminus would have to be abandoned as soon as possible. In 1895 the directors decided to proceed with the powers obtained in 1893 and extend as far as Moorgate Street. The Bank station was to be built under St. Mary Woolnoth Church. Great difficulty was experienced here, and an application was made to the Board of Trade to get possession of the crypt to start the work. An enormous sum of money—about £170,000—was eventually paid as compensation, but not until the company had taken their case to the House of Lords in 1902 and lost it there. It was thought that the church was a very strong stone structure, but it was found to be a poor shell faced to look like stone; the underpinning work had to be executed with very great care to prevent total collapse. John Mowlem & Co. were the contractors.

Temporary shafts were sunk near the Borough station to make the new junctions. London Bridge station was on the site intended for a station when the line was first made, but under the old tubes. The lines being right-handed at this point, the new ones followed the same arrangement to a point between the Bank and Moorgate Street, where the up line passed over the down, bringing the tracks to the normal left-handed position. London Bridge and the Bank stations were built on the plan afterwards common, with two station tunnels at the same level and cross passages, but the direction of running was, as it still is, the reverse of normal. Moorgate Street station, being intended to serve as a terminus for a short period only, was also built on this plan. The scissors crossing was outside in a piece of double tunnel, with a signal box on girders over the lines. After the line was opened to the Angel in 1901, the signal box was placed in the station itself. Electric lifts were adopted for the new stations, and the running tunnels were 11 ft. 6 in. diameter, in order to improve the ventilation. Apparently no advantage was felt to come from this, for this size was only used as far as Moorgate Street.

The powers to make the Clapham extension, obtained before the line was opened, had not been used, from fear of adding to the rush-hour troubles, but in 1896 it was decided to proceed, and the contract was given to W. Rigby and Co. in 1898. The intermediate station at Clapham Road (now Clapham North) and the terminus at Clapham Common had island platforms in a 30-ft.-diameter shield-driven tunnel, the largest size made on that system up to that date. Before this work was started, however, J. H. Greathead, who had been the practical initiator of the shield system, had passed away; he died at Streatham on 21 October 1896, not having lived to see London's second electric tube railway, the Waterloo & City, completed.

The last day of the King William Street terminus was 24 February 1900; on the next day, a Sunday, the trains began running over the new lines from the Borough to Moorgate Street. For a few months more Stockwell remained the southern terminus, but on Sunday, 3 June 1900, the extension to Clapham was opened. It was now possible to run four-coach trains, and everyone was heartily glad to see the end of the City station, which had proved such a bottle-neck.

New Locomotives

Experience with the first locomotives supplied had shown that improvements were needed, especially in view of the growing traffic and the proposed extensions of the line. Accordingly McMahon conducted a long series of carefully planned and recorded tests on three engines: 12, one of the original Mather & Platt engines; 15, supplied by Siemens Brothers & Co.; and 17, built by the company at Stockwell

Three locomotives built by Mather and Platt, Ltd, with the original No. 1 seen on the right. *Author's Collection*

Interior of the original electricity generating station at Stockwell. *Author's Collection*

At the Borough junction about 1920, showing the early line going to King William
Street station, just before removal

London Transport

The interior of one of the later Hurst Nelson trailer cars.   *London Transport*

Clapham Road station in 1914 showing the running times to various stations in London.   *London Transport*

The outside of Borough station in 1914.   *London Transport*

Clapham Common station about 1920.   *London Transport*

in 1895, each having certain different characteristics. These trials were followed by the conversion of 3 to a series-parallel system of control, with field shunting arrangement, and the building of three new locomotives, 18, 19, and 20, by Crompton & Co., The Electric Construction Company, and the Thames Ironworks respectively. These were delivered in 1897 and 1898; in 1899 the company built two more, 21 and 22, at Stockwell. On the basis of the experience obtained specifications were drawn up and 10 engines obtained from Crompton & Co. in 1899, ready for the extensions. The same firm supplied 10 more in 1900 and 10 more in 1901; 36 is to be seen in the concourse of Moorgate (Metropolitan line) station to-day but sheeted over after serious damage in an air raid. The general design was in appearance not very different from the original type, but was somewhat smarter; air pumps were provided for the brake system, and electric head lights. In later years 10 of the Mather & Platt engines, 3 to 12, were rebuilt at Stockwell and provided with the series-parallel control.

To provide for more economical working at quiet hours the company installed in 1895 a high-speed Willans-Siemens generating set between two of the original low-speed sets at Stockwell; this was worked with one of the old engines when two of them were not needed. A condensing plant was also added in 1896. It was seen, however, that the old power station and the two-wire system of feeding the tracks would not be satisfactory in future, and a new generating station was designed and put in hand ready for the Clapham and Moorgate extensions, with arrangements to suit the Angel extension.

This extension also was built by Rigby and Co. It was opened on 17 November 1901, with intermediate stations at Old Street and City Road (closed in 1922) and a terminal station with island platform in 30-ft. tunnel, similar to Clapham Common, at the Angel.

The distribution system adopted was a novel arrangement for traction work—a three-wire d.c. system, with 1,000 volts between the conductor rails of the up and down lines, the running rails being to earth midway between. Each terminal station was, of course, on one side only of the system, to avoid complications at crossings; there was a break in the conductor rail approaching the station where the trains passed from the positive to the negative side, or the reverse. Sub-stations at London Bridge and the Angel were fed on a 5-wire system with 2,000 volts across the outers, using balancers and boosters on the Highfield system and accumulator batteries as standby and load assisters.

This system gave entire satisfaction. The new station had 14 Davey Paxman economic boilers, working at 160-lb. pressure, feeding several engines, the principal being two compound Corliss engines by Cole, Marchant & Morley, cylinders 24 in. and 48 in. by 48 in. stroke, with built-up platework flywheels weighing 40 tons and 24-ft. diameter, driving 800-k.w. compound generators. There were also four Willans high-speed engines, driving machines of varying capacities, and, when the Angel extension was opened, a Ferranti high-speed set, replaced by a more powerful one later on. The total power of the station was 3,250 kilowatts. The original power-house was converted into a repair shop, and some of the old generator sets were used to form motor-generators in the new building.

New Carriage Stock

Additions to the original stock of 30 carriages had been made in 1891, 1894, 1896, 1897, 1899, and 1901, bringing the total up to 124 at the time of the Islington extension. Eight more coaches were obtained in 1902. All these were, with small general improvements, of generally similar design, but when the extension to Euston was opened in 1907 the Brush Company provided 30 all-steel-type vehicles, which were a great improvement on the earlier type. Five-car trains were introduced about 1906. In order to bring stock to the surface at Stockwell without having to use the steep incline tunnel, a hydraulic lift was brought into use in 1906, able to take one coach or loco-motive at a time. The underground sidings there were gradually much extended and, with those at other places, such as Clapham Common, enabled examination and ordinary repair work to be attended to below ground.

The growth of the traffic on the line from the opening to the end of the company's independent existence is shown in the following table:

City & South London Railway: Passenger Journeys, Receipts, and Ordinary Dividends in Certain Years, 1891-1911

Year	Number of Passengers Carried	Receipts £	Miles Open for Traffic	Ordinary Capital Issued £	Dividend on Ordinary Stock per cent
1891	5,362,950	39,202	3.12	630,000	nil
1896	6,913,712	49,478	3.12	630,000	1-9/16
1901	13,412,676	110,749	6.9	1,330,000	2
1906	19,491,013	144,682	6.9	1,480,000	2¼
1911	26,159,461	172,908	7.26	1,480,000	1⅝

The highest dividend on City & South London Railway ordinary stock was 3¼ per cent., for the year 1902.

The old turnstile system had been given up when the Moorgate extension was opened in 1900, and the customary ticket system with graduated fares was introduced. With the opening of other tube lines, through bookings were introduced, and a subway connection to the Brighton station was provided at London Bridge.

In 1898 an act was passed authorising the construction of a City & Brixton Railway, which proposed to use the old King William Street station and tunnels for the first part of its course. This seems a little curious, seeing the trouble that station had caused and the supposed impossibility of enlarging it. No capital was ever raised, however, for this line, and the City & South London Company proposed to take over the powers, ease the gradients on the old route, and make another station beneath the original terminus, with subway to the Central London Bank station, and a second London Bridge station underneath the one opened in 1900, so as to afford an alternative route for some of its trains to the City. Nothing ever came of this plan, and the City & Brixton project lapsed entirely. The King William

Street station therefore remained derelict until converted
into an air-raid shelter in the 1939 war.

Interchanges and Developments

The general offices of the line were transferred to Moorgate Street in 1900. In 1899 an agreement had been con-
cluded with the Great Northern & City Railway (Moorgate
Street and Finsbury Park) for a joint station at Old Street,
which came into effect when that line was opened in
February 1904. The interchange traffic proved satisfactory, but by that time the effects of electric tramway
competition began to make themselves felt and went on
increasing as the various routes of the London County
Council system were electrified.

In 1902 a bill was independently promoted for a Euston
& Islington Railway, but it failed to pass. In the next
year, with the backing of the City & South London
Company, and in its name, a similar bill was successful,
and a contract was awarded to Walter Scott &
Middleton in 1904. In 1906 a subway connection was
opened with the Baker Street & Waterloo Railway at the
Elephant.

Charles Grey Mott, chairman of the undertaking from
its inception, died on 7 November 1905, aged 72. Elected a
director of the Great Western Railway in 1868, he had
been associated with a number of railway companies at
home and abroad. It was he, it would seem, who first had
doubts whether cable traction would prove satisfactory and
induced his colleagues to consider the adoption of electrical
working. In this he showed sound judgment. The railway
could not possibly have succeeded as it did if cable haulage
had been used, because the average speed would have
been far too low to enable it to afford a satisfactory service
to the public. The vacant chair was taken by the Rt.
Hon. C. B. Stuart-Wortley, a director of the Great Central
Railway.

About the time the extension to Moorgate was opened
in 1900, the company began to install two very valuable
improvements, afterwards followed on all the London
tubes, by fixing lights in the tunnels at 50-ft. intervals,
which a signalman could switch on if a train was an

unusually long time in section, and bare conducting wires from station to station, with telephone sets on the loco-motives, by which a driver of a disabled train, or one held for an unusual time at a signal, could communicate with the signalman in advance or in rear, to advise him of the position of the train and ask for assistance if required, or for the current to be cut off. The accumulator battery arrangements at the sub-stations assured the constant supply to the tunnel lights.

The Euston extension had two stations, King's Cross for St. Pancras, of the type then usual, and Euston, with an island platform in a 30-ft. tube, similar to the Angel and Clapham Common stations. The lifts at King's Cross brought passengers right down to platform level. At Euston there was a subway to the London & North-Western station and the Charing Cross, Euston & Hampstead line, and a station building, of rather ornate style, in white and green stone, in Seymour Street*; this has since disappeared, part of Euston House now occupying the site. At Weston Street, Pentonville Hill, there was an emergency shaft with stairs and a signal box in a cross passage between the two tubes, with outer and inner home signals in each direction, and the usual tunnel light and telephone com-munication apparatus. Short down gradients were pro-vided here to assist trains in starting. The trains attained a good rate of speed on the up line after leaving the Angel, the general gradient being a falling one, and the sudden rush down these signal dips was very noticeable. It can still be detected, although it seems less pronounced since the line was rebuilt.

This extension was formally opened on 11 May 1907, by the chairman of the London County Council, Sir Percy Harris, and to the public on the following day; it brought the railway into close connection with important main-line termini and greatly increased its usefulness, but it did not improve the financial position of the undertaking, which continued to give cause for some anxiety. In 1909, largely at the request of the Great Northern & City Railway, it was decided to begin the service on Sundays at 8.15 a.m. instead of 11.40. Receipts continued to fall, however,

* Now Eversholt Street.

notwithstanding the attempts made to accelerate and improve the service and use more powerful locomotives.

Control by the Underground Group

Faced with this position, the board came to terms with the Underground Electric Railways Company of London, Ltd., and in 1913 the C. & S.L.R. passed into their financial control, 99 per cent. of the ordinary stock being transferred. The chairman resigned and three of the directors retired, S. Barclay Heward, Edwin Tate, and J. F. S. Gooday (formerly general manager of the Great Eastern and Brighton lines, who had succeeded H. Ranking in 1911), their place being taken by Sir A. H. Stanley (later Lord Ashfield), Admiral Sir Cyprian Bridge, and Mr. T. C. Jenkin, until then general manager. The Board recorded that Mr. Jenkin had "displayed a degree of vigilance, courtesy, and organising capacity which it would be difficult to overpraise". He remained a director until his death in November 1920.

The principal immediate effect of the change, so far as the public was concerned, was the introduction of non-stop trains, which ran through certain stations, such as Clapham Road, Kennington, Borough, and City Road. A bill was then promoted, and received the assent of Parliament in 1913, for enlarging the tunnels to enable standard-size Underground trains to run over the line, and another bill, promoted by the London Electric Railway, was passed for the construction of a connecting line from Euston to the Hampstead & Highgate line at Camden Town. Only preliminary planning had been done when the war of 1914 stopped the scheme. In the next year the Stockwell power station was closed and the line fed from the Underground's Lots Road station, with sub-stations at Stockwell, Elephant, Old Street, and Euston (joint with the Hampstead line); the sub-stations opened at London Bridge and Angel in 1900 and 1901 were closed. The third-rail voltage was raised from 500 to 550.

At the end of the war it was hoped to proceed with reconstruction, but circumstances proved too difficult. The line had some trouble in carrying on efficiently, and the coal strike made matters worse. It was short of both staff and rolling stock, and it became necessary to close some stations earlier than usual and others all day on Sundays; train intervals were also increased, and fares were raised about 40 per cent. To improve the running during the rush hours, track-circuit automatic signalling was put in to replace the original mechanical signalling and Spagnoletti interlocking block, which proved an obstacle to the successful working of non-stop trains; these were often pulled up, or nearly so, unnecessarily, owing to the time lost in going through the manual signalling movements. There were no automatic train stops, however; to fit them to the locomotives and in the small tunnels would have been very difficult, if, indeed, possible at all. There were always two men on the engines, and there was not the same need for such equipment as elsewhere.

The reconstruction work was not actually begun until the autumn of 1922, under the Trade Facilities Act, 1921, which authorised the issue of £2,700,000 4½ per cent special debenture stock. It was decided to close only that part of the line between Euston and Moorgate Street in August and to keep traffic running on the remainder. The chief feature of the enlargement work, and the one which made it economically possible, was that, except on the short piece from the Borough junction to the Elephant where the 10-ft. 2-in. tunnels remained, the retention and re-use of the original cast-iron lining was possible; this was still as sound as when it was put in. Four extra segment pieces, resembling the key pieces, were used to enable the old segments to form the new tunnel of slightly irregular shape, but effectively 11 ft. 8¼ in. in diameter, the Underground standard. The rolling stock being so small, it was possible to make a shield through which the trains could pass, and about 85 per cent. of the 10 ft. 6 in. and 10 ft. 2 in. tunnels were enlarged by that means, which considerably shortened the time required for the work. On the 11 ft. 6 in. tunnels from the Borough junction to Moorgate Street the work was done without a shield, the two bottom segments remaining undisturbed over a considerable length.

During 1919 and 1920, while the scheme was in abeyance, an experimental length of 180 yds. of tunnel near Stockwell was enlarged by using a shield, to test the practicability of the plan. The Moorgate to Euston section was done by contract by Perry and Co. (Bow), Ltd. and Charles Brand, Ltd., and the tunnels were handed over to them towards the end of 1922. The southern section was done by the Underground staff, except that mining labour was provided by Walter Scott & Middleton, Ltd. The sidings at Kennington and the crossover tunnel were carried out by Charles Brand, and the enlargement of Clapham Road and Clapham Common stations by the Metropolitan Tunnel & Public Works Co. Work on this section was directed from the Stockwell depot; Stockwell and the Borough stations were closed in August 1922. Kennington was closed in June 1923. Sidings were put in where the Borough platforms had been, and the whole station converted into a depot and work site. Water-bearing ground between Stockwell and the Oval made compressed-air working necessary, so only one line could be dealt with at a time; to allow of this, temporary crossover tunnels were built at Portland Place and South Island Place, in the Clapham Road, shortening the distances over which single line train working had to be put into force. The track-circuit automatic signalling which had by then been put in greatly facilitated this working, which would have involved complicated controls with the old manual apparatus. The train service was altered to begin at 6.20 a.m. and end at 8.0 p.m., and special buses were put on the route to lessen inconvenience. One of the most delicate features of the work was avoiding all damage to the power and signalling cables along the tunnels, which had to be kept in service, especially the 11,000-volt feeders to the sub-stations. The rate of progress naturally varied with local difficulties, but as many as 24 tunnel rings per week (40 ft.) were handled at times. In all 14 shields and 6 hand-excavated tunnel faces were worked simultaneously from the Stockwell depot. Much of the tool and other equipment was specially designed to be left along the tunnel sides during the day. After a fall which took place at the point where the lines crossed between Borough and the Elephant on 27 November 1923, single-line working was introduced between Stockwell and London Bridge, but as this did not allow of anything like normal facilities being given, it was decided to close the

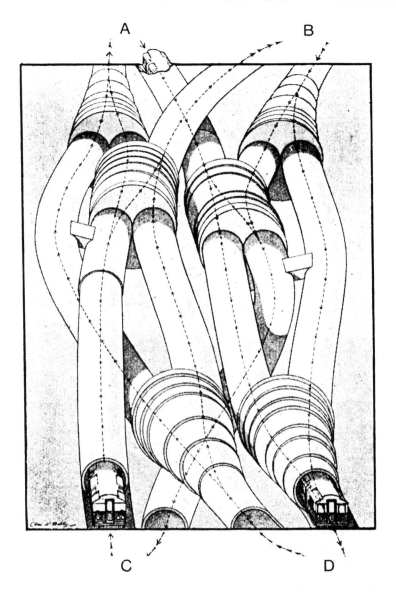

Diagramatic arrangement of tubes at Camden Town in 1922.

A– *To and from*–Camden Town, Chalk Farm, Belsize Park, Hampstead, Golder's Green, Brent, Hendon (Central), Colindale, Burnt Oak and Edgware.

B– *To and from*–Camden Town, South Kentish Town, Kentish Town, Tufnell Park and Highgate.

C– *To and from*–Euston (C & SLR), King's Cross, Angel, Old Street and Moorgate.

D– *To and from*–Euston (LER), Warren Street, Goodge Street, Tottenham Court Road, Leicester Square, Strand and Charing Cross.

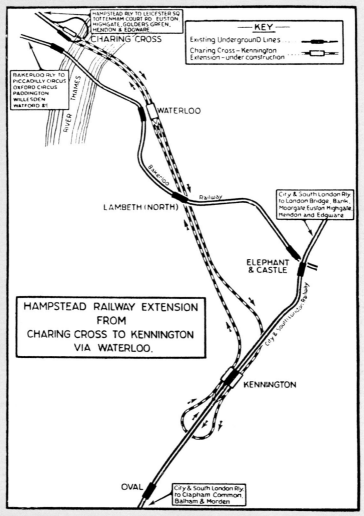

Sections through the original City and South London Railway tunnel and the tunnel as reconstructed to pass standard Underground stock.

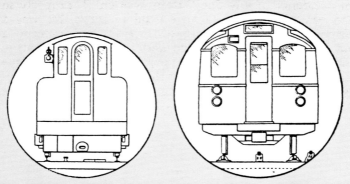

railway altogether not long afterwards. Work was then pressed forward without interruption. The suspension of train services allowed some realignments to be effected, such as at the Elephant and Kennington, where the up line was moved over to the opposite side of the platform, itself moved correspondingly in the other direction. Many other detailed improvements were made.

In December 1923, during the reconstruction, powers were obtained to extend the railway from Clapham to Morden. On 20 April 1924 the northern portion from Euston to Moorgate Street, with connection to Camden Town, was reopened, and the rest of the route from Moorgate to Clapham Common on 1 December, marking the termination of a fine piece of civil engineering. On 13 September 1926, the line was extended to Morden, with stations at Clapham South, Balham, Trinity Road (Tooting Bec), Tooting Broadway, Colliers Wood, South Wimbledon (Merton), and Morden. On the same day the connecting line authorised in 1924 from Charing Cross (Hampstead line) through Waterloo to Kennington, with additional platforms parallel with the City & South London platforms and junctions beyond was also brought into service. On 1 March 1927 a short connecting line was made between the Piccadilly line and the northbound line of the City & South London at King's Cross, for interchange of rolling stock. The last important improvement, sanctioned in 1929, was a subway with escalators from the Bank station to the District line Monument station. The passing of the undertaking to the London Passenger Transport Board in 1933 marked the end of the line as a concern with a title of its own.

Accidents

The City & South London Railway was remarkably free from accidents. Only one " train accident ", properly so called, was the subject of an official inquiry; this was a collision on 26 September 1900. A train had come to a stand between London Bridge and Bank from armature failure, and the following train passed the Bank outer home signal at danger. The driver of the colliding train and his assistant were clearly not looking ahead at all; even if the signal had been irregularly at clear for them they could easily have stopped, as the lights of the standing train were in full view for some distance.

A few other accidents, not train accidents, also were inquired into. As one of the lifts at London Bridge, on the newly opened Moorgate Street extension, was about to descend on 28 June 1900, an overhead counterweight pulley shaft broke, and the cage went down very rapidly and struck the bottom buffers so violently that some counterweights resting on girders over the lift, used to adjust the balance of the cage, fell off and crashed through the roof, causing serious injury to three people. It was found that the safety catch gear was out of operation while some repairs were being made; this caused strong comment from the Inspecting Officer, though even if it had been in working position it would not have been effective in the circumstances. The pulley shaft had been weakened by the addition of some set screws which started a flaw. The design was in consequence improved.

Another lift accident occurred, at the Oval station, on 2 August 1909. As the cage, with 44 passengers, was being lowered a copper pipe in the hydraulic equipment failed, and the lift descended the last 13 ft. very quickly; the shock at stopping caused some damage to electric lamps and glass fittings. Six passengers were cut or bruised, and water from the burst pipe deluged the lift.

Early on Sunday, 24 May 1908, fire broke out in Clapham Common station, and a locomotive was destroyed. As the service did not begin until 11.30 a.m. the night watchman had, as was customary, gone off duty at 3.0 a.m. The origin of the fire was not known for certain, but the Inspecting Officer remarked that it had been useful as a test and the fact that the carriage coupled to the engine had escaped was " a point in favour of separate locomotives ". Another fire occurred at the end of the crossover tunnel at Moorgate Street station on 16 July 1908, near the disused signal box. It was found that much of the dust in the tunnels was of a dangerous character, very easily ignited.

Two fatal accidents seem never to have been reported officially, as no record of them is to be found at the Ministry of Transport. According to brief statements in the press, a passenger was killled in June 1892 in unusual circumstances. A guard was in the habit of inviting people to go out on the front platform of the leading coach to " watch the engine at work "; this passenger fell into the tunnel and was cut to pieces. The guard was so terrified that he hid himself and was not found for some time. In July 1891 a passenger was killed at the Oval station. The liftman started the lift with the gates still open (there was no automatic control then to prevent that on the original lifts); the passenger jumped and forced himself partly in; the disturbance prevented the liftman from stopping again in time, and the intruder was decapitated against the cross-girder of the entrance.

*   *   *

The changes that have taken place in underground locomotion in London in the 65 years that have elapsed since the public first travelled under the Thames in an electric train in the original City & South London tunnels have no doubt been more profound and of more far-reaching effect than could ever have been imagined by the promoters of the City of London & Southwark Subway. Nevertheless, they owe their origins to the courage and enterprise of those who, confident in Greathead's judgment and ability, found the money to construct the line and to extend it, and adopted electric traction in place of cable haulage—a decisive step towards its final success. The number of those who can remember the inauguration of the undertaking and the old City terminus in its original condition is now small; but a good many traces of the original line are to be found by the observant along its course, and locomotives and rolling stock survive at the Science Museum and at the Railway Museum at York.

The idea of London today without its electric tube railways is unthinkable. Their story in the early days is one of trial and error, of wise and unwise experiments and decisions; and on the whole the unwise ones were few. As the pioneer, the City & South London had to make its mistakes; but it was bold and resilient, and its part in developing the technique of the modern London tube system was an honourable one.

APPENDIX

LOCOMOTIVES

Nos.	Builders				Date
1 to 14	Mather & Platt	..	..	..	..	1889–1890
15, 16	Siemens Brothers	..	..	..	..	1891
17	Stockwell Works	..	..	..	..	1895
18	Crompton & Co.	..	..	..		⎫
19	Electric Construction Co.	..	..	..		⎬ 1897–1898
20	Thames Ironworks		..	..	..	⎭
21	Stockwell Works	..	..	..	..	1899
22	Stockwell Works	..	..	..	..	1900
23 to 32	Crompton & Co.	..	..	..	..	1899
33 to 42	Crompton & Co.	..	..	..	..	1900
43 to 52	Crompton & Co.	..	..	..	..	1901

The motor-coach train tried in 1894 appears to have been constructed at Stockwell Works; no manufacturer is spoken of in any reference to it.

ROLLING STOCK

Nos.	Builders			Date
1 to 30	Ashbury Carriage & Iron Co.	..	..	1889–1890
31 to 36	G. F. Milnes and Co.	..	..	..	1891
37 to 39	Bristol Carriage & Wagon Co.	..	..	1894
40 to 46	Oldbury Carriage & Wagon Co.		..	1896
47 to 54	G. F. Milnes and Co.	..	..	..	1897
55 to 84	Hurst Nelson & Co.	..	..	..	1899
85 to 108	G. F. Milnes & Co...	..	..	..	1901
109 to 124	Bristol Carriage & Wagon Co.	..	..	1901
125 to 132	G. F. Milnes & Co...	..	..	..	1902
133 to 165	Brush Electrical Engineering Co.	..	..	1907
(All-steel type)				

At the conversion of the line the locomotives were scrapped, with the exception of two. Of these one carrying the number plate " No. 1 " (not the original engine carrying that number), of the type used at the opening of the railway, is now in the Science Museum, South Kensington, painted in the original livery. No. 36, constructed by Crompton & Co. and delivered in 1900, was reconditioned and stood for some time, in the fine yellow lined livery adopted after the line had been opened a year or two, on a pedestal at Moorgate station, Metropolitan line. It was very badly damaged in an air-raid during the 1939 war, but is still in place, painted plain grey, and sheeted over. It is understood that it will eventually be restored to its former condition. Of the carriages, one of the original " padded cell " form, No. 10, was reconditioned and is in the York Railway Museum. The others were scrapped, although one or two found their way into private hands for summer houses, etc. No. 39 is to be seen at Watlington, Oxon.

AUTHORITIES

Apart from the financial information given in the annual volumes of *Bradshaw's Railway Manual* and the company meetings reported in the daily and railway papers, the following are the principal authorities for the technical history of the City & South London Railway:

Proceedings of the Institution of Civil Engineers.

Edward Hopkinson, ELECTRICAL RAILWAYS: THE CITY & SOUTH LONDON RAILWAY (read 14 February 1893), Vol. 121 (1892-3), pt. 2, p. 1.

J. H. Greathead, THE CITY & SOUTH LONDON RAILWAY, WITH RE-MARKS ON SUB-AQUEOUS TUNNELING BY SHIELD AND COMPRESSED AIR (read 19 November 1895), Vol. 123 (1895-6), pt. 1, p. 39.

I. J. Jones and G. Curry, ENLARGEMENT OF THE CITY & SOUTH LONDON RAILWAY TUNNELS (read 5 April 1927), Vol. 224 (1926-7), pt. 2, p. 176.

Proceedings of the Institution of Electrical Engineers.

P. V. McMahon, ELECTRIC LOCOMOTIVES IN PRACTICE AND TRACTIVE RESISTANCE IN TUNNELS, WITH NOTES ON ELECTRIC LOCOMOTIVE DESIGN (read 4 May 1899), Vol. 28 (1899), p. 508; and THE CITY & SOUTH LONDON RAILWAY: WORKING RESULTS OF THE THREE-WIRE SYSTEM APPLIED TO TRACTION, etc. (read 17 December 1903), Vol. 33 (1904), p. 100.

Proceedings of the Institution of Railway Signal Engineers.

W. S. Every, SIGNALLING ON THE LONDON UNDERGROUND RAILWAYS (read 12 November 1924), Session 1924-5, pt. 2, p. 154.

T. S. Lascelles, EARLY TUBE RAILWAY SIGNALLING, Session 1941, p. 40.

In addition, the following general descriptions have been published: *The Railway Gazette:* JUBILEE OF THE CITY & SOUTH LONDON RAILWAY (13 December 1940); LOCOMOTIVES OF THE CITY & SOUTH LONDON RAILWAY (6 March 1942); *The Railway Magazine:* ILLUSTRATED INTERVIEW with T. C. Jenkin (5 (1899), 1); H. L. Hopwood, THE WORLD'S PIONEER TUBE RAILWAY (47 (1920), 363); T. S. Lascelles, DIAMOND JUBILEE OF THE CITY & SOUTH LONDON RAILWAY (97 (1951), 129); *Cassier's Magazine,* Electric Railway Number (1899), P. V. McMahon, THE CITY & SOUTH LONDON ELECTRIC RAILWAY.

ACKNOWLEDGMENTS

The author is much indebted to the following for valuable advice and assistance, especially for permission to examine old records, drawings and photographs: the late Mr. J. A. Kay, formerly Editor of *The Railway Gazette;* Mr. B. W. C. Cooke, the present Editor, for kindly providing the map; the late Lt.-Colonel Sir Alan Mount, formerly Chief Inspecting Officer of Railways; Lt.-Colonel G. R. S. Wilson, the present holder of that office; Mr. C. G. Page, Secretary to the London Passenger Transport Board; Mr. Michael Robbins, Secretary to its successor, the London Transport Executive; Mr. T. E. Haywood, at one time in the service of Messrs. Dutton & Co., Worcester; Mr. Charles E. Lee, Tothill Press Ltd., Vice-President of The Railway Club; Mr. C. Follenfant, formerly on the engineering staff of the City & South London Railway; Mr. A. Jenkin, son of the late Mr. T. C. Jenkin, first General Manager of the line; Mr. Alexander McDonald, Secretary of the Institution of Civil Engineers; Messrs. Mather & Platt, Ltd.; Messrs. Crompton-Parkinson, Ltd.; Messrs. Siemens Brothers & Co., Ltd.; Messrs. Cole Marchant & Morley (1929), Ltd.; Messrs. The Electric Construction Co. Ltd.